To
Dr. Gold.
Wishing positive
prosperity above &
beyond measure for re——
Unconditional love for rea——
distant galaxies. Enlightment——
in to your world.

Moon: ♡

A Journey

Not A Destination

A Self-Portrait of Life Inspired Writings

Moon

A Journey Not A Destination

All Right Reserved.
Copyright© 2019 Moon Goddess Publishing
Cover/Back photo courtesy of JustSoDucky
Varied Photos, Sketches & Clipart
Cover design: Dominique K. Howard
Image credit: Mark Garcia:
www.PointBlankBx.com

ISBN: 978-1-7345962-9-8

DEDICATION

First and foremost, The Creator; In infinite wisdom for the diverse blessings, lessons and experiences.

Dominique (daughter) and Joshua (son): never a burden but the greatest of gifts.

The wide-ranging muses which presented themselves throughout an exploratory journey.

Finally, the front and back cover in Loving Memory of Marcia A. Berry-Diggs; *"I love you dear lady and will miss our Fearless Friday walks to The Little Red Lighthouse."*

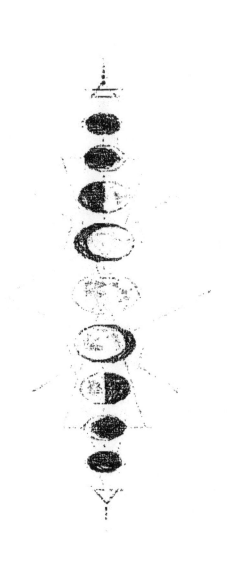

TABLE OF CONTENTS

PROLOGUE

Communication and self-expression are undoubtedly the most important skills to hone. Being able to communicate clearly and effectively in our own environment and comfort zone may seem challenging. However, they are increasingly exponential in different cultures and all types of relationships.

There are two parts of communication which always hold true no matter what our cultural background. Verbal and nonverbal communication exists regardless of surrounding environments. Some have physical, spiritual and emotional presence. Writing requires a particular set of self-expressive skills that not everyone possess. Does that mean that other persons do not have something useful or interesting to say? Absolutely not.

There are many topics, genre, media forms which can be covered under the umbrella of communiqué. Such as, in the beginning of a program attended: Clemente Bridge. We were instructed to draw images of how we see ourselves then write affirmations: "*I am....*" The image and every word of that self-portrait journey established a public definition of particular times and aspects of life through this manuscript. Wherein, writing being able to express things powerless to be spoken; Due to emotional rejection or physical harm. Identify or acknowledge the journey.

I am...: The focus of the pieces in this project which includes: Love, loss, growth, erotica, muses and recovery. All these things encompass every facet of my *spiritual being, living a human experience*. Some may feel these as just words on a page. They are feelings, emotions, which express followings, fortes and faiths of daily living or survival through emotive mechanisms or perceptions of who *I am...*

Some have viewed my writings as one of my greatest strengths with its abundance of ideas. In addition, with time much more interesting than the concepts or observations used to be. Often, many thoughts flow through my head at any given moment that it may be difficult to jot them all down on paper or type before new ones take their place.

The most essential components needed in order to be at one with self: experience, strength and hope. Experience serves as the source of many philosophies that can help complete a "survival kit" - skills and techniques that will allow us (me) to function. Although, not everyone immersions in life the same way, each and every one of us has basic knowledge that serves as their "survival kit". Every "survival kit" possesses some notions that will help someone manage a situation for the first time or as a reference point.

We are all works in progress of some kind. Sometimes despite the phenomenal involvement or lack thereof... There are things that are connected to us that are left behind not progressing or cannot go along with the next phase of life. Each person's journey; if we are willing, teaches us how to find the necessary peace and serenity to successfully merge or emerge. It is either; one is so dominant that the other one's only option is to follow and obey or the other is being suppressed to dull a shine, left not helped and despised

All in all, every program or individual on the journey was beneficial, especially in extremely difficult moments after time and reflection. The effort in these writings may attest to a foundational start too eventually become willing through varied reflections of self. The question arises; Have we effectively and adequately depicted explicit themes as an open channel of a self-portrait journey by means of show casing these specific fragments to represent this episode of development?

"Action is the foundational key to life; Remember why we started. A realistic self-portrait is not a destination; it's a continuous journey that never ends. An expedition of self, is never-ending or until there is no remembrance of us."

Note: Contains explicit language

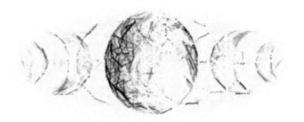

R.I.P.

"Nothing will come of nothing." ~Shakespeare

ADDICTED

An intoxicating elixir
A hallucinogenic drug
Above and beyond any of its effects
You are my high

You heal me
Continue to thrill me
Utter ecstasy
Chills me to the bone

No need to search
Our adventure doesn't linger
Only thriving striving
It presses on

Each day more exciting
Captivating
Loving your present
An ultimate gift

ARTIST IN PURE LOVE

Paint delicate pictures thru my soul
Creating landscapes of immeasurable beauty
Our connection transcends the physical

A place where spiritual plateau rests
Far beyond the reaches of moon and stars
Your voice sings a song
Playing deep within since the dawn of time.
Tender chills enrapture my entire body
Your fingertips: A mere brush across my face
I climb high

Your love and encouragement firmly planted
NOT a moment goes by...
You're a part of every thought
Every movement.
Never in all my life have I known a light so pure
A light so true
Light just right.

Love is for those believers,
Who walks it?
Who lives it?
I believe in such a love
I walk in this love
I live this love with every breath
A pure love
I can show you better than I can tell you.

A CLUE

Don't even know
Not even a clue
Abundant feelings
World in hand
However, need of understanding
Really hunger & yearn approval

Holding others down
Just to be in vicinity
Just contemplate...
Hoping senses open
Realize, before it's too late

Not like what's used to
Give flowers not make less than
Greatest listener, creative empathetic
No problem excessive or minute
Resolutions the goal
Virtuous to the best of abilities

Should plans made?
Just some sort of fool?
Gotten pretty damn close
Recognize hesitation, not to let farther in...
Let go of past, truly see
Realization of a highly capabilities being

Sure, there have been others
Others who made promises
Touched deep places spaces
Sparked special feelings
Just like all only sent us reeling

(continued next page)

Some days just going through the motions
Would NEVER stray
Wanting to be kept near, dearest
Never, any intent to hurt
Just be deserving of a chance

Like NO other use too
Like NO other one day distinguish
No mere line or statement of conceit
Ready to show... LOVE
What love can & supposed to be
Inquiring... Let heart be open, free

NEW BEGINNINGS

The waters of our love - thinking, oh so deep
We jumped in anyways
Just for the nights we got to keep
      I hoped maybe you'd stay

        Maybe you'd love me like
        you once did them
        Hope lingers in my heart.
          I couldn't leave things the
            way they were...
          I call you, I want to restart

    Now.
  I'm alone...
    Thinking of earlier nights
      I wonder how strong you feel
        If it was a mistake.
        The love sure felt right
        Now it's at its end

        The heart isn't broken
        They say, "It does heal."
        It beats if willing...
        To only begin again

WANDERING FEELINGS

How silence roars in the dead of night
It's how a deceitful voice may seem
A saddening smile reflecting life
A hidden plot, script or scheme

Feelings of loneliness conquer
Mind & heart with tidal waves of lies
Lies which wander through forbidden streets
Amongst midnight cries

The manner of a whisper in a crowd
Makes one more afraid
Darkening eyes which see through all
Cut like sharpened blades

Feelings of sadness wrestling down
Oh, shallow words of steel
Wander through deserted lands
Never to heal

GIFT

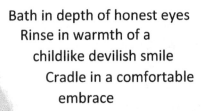

Bath in depth of honest eyes
Rinse in warmth of a
childlike devilish smile
Cradle in a comfortable
embrace

The rapture of
such visions
Words-mentally
spiritually stimulating
Sheltering many storms
through tender kisses

Sunshine or rain; Pleasurable pain
Never thought in this time
Too skip or ring in a single positive chime

(continued next page)

Music succinct
Knowing every rhyme

Up/down
round/round
Rollercoaster
merry-go-round
Emotions –
waver
shake
quiver
quake
our core

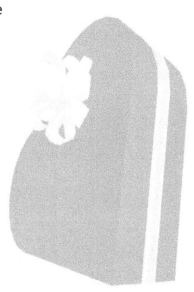

Hot & Cold
Pressure Bust
Shatter
Break pipes

Together repair
Keeping the
other safe
Thanks for
presence
A gift; strength of
character to
being woke

FEAR

Afraid of what's felt
Knowing it's real

Touches in places
Fill all the spaces
Nothing to be left inside
This cannot be
Here? How? Why?

There is so much feared
Will there be lies or cheating?
If so, death is welcomed

Although, all caught up
Heart stuck - is all too soon, right?
The aching collapsing

Just so confused
Don't want to be used
Please Creator help!

What's this about?
Thought, ready?
This man... just so not ready

Soul in turmoil unsteady
Don't want to be dropped

Is this love found
Need to be sheltered
Need to be undisputable?

Cuz this is too much
I pine for their touch
Please ease fears uncertainties
Decisions secure, concrete

NEED vs WANT

In need of someone to share all dreams
That someone special
Just one who will love just for love
Is it something needed or wanted?

In need of someone to hold tight
To give good sweet loving all night
So many times, too have opened up one's heart
Only to have someone tear it apart

Just someone to treat a woman right
Make love when needed, right
What wants and needs
We've all been hurt before, real love
Real love, is it a dream and/or fantasy?
Such a vision essential and earnest of...

It would be nice to have one just one
Who will never leave a woman feeling lonely?
Someone faithful, who'll love as their one and only

Someone to share ups and downs
Especially in those extremely bad times: be around
Again & again opening up all of a faith heart
Only to have it torn apart
Not what anyone wants or needs

Why can't there be that special one to treat right?
That love so real
Making-love fantasizing dreaming
Oh, all through the day or night
An unconditional love; that's a need vs want

REPLACED

There will be NO tears
Perhaps a sigh of relief
They are replaceable?

Just like others
Bangin' bodies the model type
No distinctive marks

Extremely fine
Somewhat kind, heavenly
There are others

Positive when it started
Preference to ride solo
Truly one's own

A distant memory
Long gone really soon
No regrets, just replaced

Replaced by time
Back to having space
No worries but their own

In the back of the mind
A fraud
They all are...

(*continued next page*)

No distractions
No one in mind
No excuses, it's what is chosen

All one needs
A short amount of time
Just continue to grind

Better days ahead
A new year
New destinations

Beautiful people in exotic spaces
All with their own erotic traces
Cuz everyone can be replaced???

EASILY FORGOTTEN

Footsteps ahead of me
One set, alone
They are deep
As my soul & spirit in sadness

They're scattered shattered
Back to the dance
Though the party is alone
Still in step & time

The path winding
The trees all stand tall
The sun shines on my toes
And the hurt
One day will be easily forgotten

LONG WALK HOME

Defective approval validation
Wishing to be the one
One chosen
If left today
Needing time space
Would there be a chase?

Tomorrow a fleeting memory
Any tears?
A brief sigh?
Even wonder
Wonder why?

Once, wrapped in warmth
In wait of the question... Stay?
It doesn't happen
A walk not alone to home

Cold...calculating
The thoughts which may have been...
An ultimate spine chiller
Shivers envelope
Icy judgement fills the mind

Once euphoric
Now a walk of guilt, shame, remorse
Seemly, demeaning
The wait... Anticipation of warmth
Home a safe haven

(*continued next page*)

I cry for us
It doesn't help
We don't come back
  I think...
Maybe, I'll wake up
It's all been a nightmare
  But it's reality

In a corner
Sit alone and afraid
Face – it shows a smile
Yet tears flow monsoon rains

Inside a heart riddled with pain
The memories are so painful
How is it jokes, laughter & fun?
Can make one feel they want to die?
Wanting needing it behind
It's there in front between the two of us

The avoided glances
The calls that will never be made
The security lost never to be found
Why leave? Verve away?
Only for crying turned sheer anguish
Praying the laughter once will return

LOVE STORY

We are writers of love & erotic stories.

Loving beyond every word known to (wo)man.

Loving more than every grain: salt or sand.

Loving deeper than the ocean: vast & deep.

Loving beyond galaxies; existing in far-off systems.

Loving more infinite then finite.

Loving deeper than conditions.

Loving beyond an arcs end.

Some reality, others dreams with fantasy.

It's our decision; the reader - which is which...

However, Love unconditionally

Every second, minute, hour... chance we get...

Don't forget to ... ***Breathe***!!!

For, Tomorrow is NOT promised...

Growing

"Be who you are and say what you feel, because those who mind don't matter and those who matter don't mind."

~ Dr. Seuss

There is a war being waged

Guardian? Gargoyle?

Pride ego stoking, fueling fires
Anger, Resentment, Guilt & Shame

A truth, Hope, Humility & Empathy
Both putting up a good fight

Lots of blame going round-n-round
Contentment none to be found

Continually wearing a mask
Nowhere to set it down

Misunderstanding of purity
Cradle of civilization the true crown

Outside inside issues casting shade
Willing to play an unsuspecting clown

Why?
A plague?

Society should want or need us all
Possess a sane clear woke mind

OBSESSION WITH FIRE

Obsession with fire
Wanting a love that burns
Bright as the sun
Luminous blood moon

Feel the heat
Emotions which churn
Whirling tornados
cyclones lots
Wreckage of a storm

Ash & cinder – Eventually Regrowth
Charred heart
Beating yet yearns
Flawed opportunities

Promises, plans forgotten
Deserted lands
Sodom & Gomorrah
Thoughts shunned & scorned

Burn Baby Burn
"Let the Motherfucker Burn"
What love-life & life
In years past have been...

CHILDLIKE: SIMPLE MIND

Walking this life
  Given by The Creator
    Wanting to be uncomplicated

Creator, Please Grant

Tried true loyalty & honesty
  Not just one who says...
    They understand!

A good girl
  No, a gifted Goddess
    A spiritual, yet Earthly woman

Mind having no grand schemes
  Or far-fetched plans
    Childlike simple mind

Job... Love & support
  A bit of witty retort
    Don't make life games or sports

Games are played, some masters
  As others indulge
    Why bother?

Not meant to walk alone
  Isolated all on own our own
    A path of growth & undemanding

Another request
  Creator, beg you're the one
    Guide heart & head

(continued next page)

It took being clean & sober
  To understand
  Not a war or destination

Eventually rewarded
  Find self; truly where, what, who we are...
    An intricate part of an others head & heart

Their loving arms & feet
  Strengthening the other
    When physically, mentally, spiritually weak
It's what The Creator
  Be-witchingly: Shown & told so...
    It's not a dream or fantasy

Given positive wealth
  Above beyond measure
    King or Master

Creator and thee
  Damn sure...
    Never let...

A negative thought idea inkling
    Be in defense or question: Yes, you matter
    Not cuz of need or wanted validation

All deserving of every positive
    Life has in store or offers
    Not just words on paper or pages

Written in any simple or special book
  Shedding optimistic vibrations
    Life defying comprehension

It far exceeds the greatest of any expectations

KARMIC RETRIBUTION

Tortured tormented heart
Dismal dank soul

Guessing Karmic retribution
Soul burning, Earthly hell fire

Maybe in a past life
Brazen flirtation behavior

No fault coverage
Insurance denied pain

Lessons a mockery
No saint, just sinner

Found guilty
Wanting a love

Speak in tongues
Foul fool to think otherwise

ROAMING THOUGHTS

Lonely but not alone
Thoughts dream fantasy
Guide to a home

A home of love & desire
Waltz tango salsa rumba
Ballerina of grace

Whether apart or whole
Loves purest heart
Has one sold

An ideology
A bill of sell
Keep faith & hope

Hope springs eternal
A lifetime of happiness
One day to be true

Enlightenment of positivity
Universe a cavern
Rarest treasures not guaranteed

Artisan of space
Time love desires happiness not linear
Their spell continually going on...

A WALK WITH SOMEONE

We walk this life
Given by The Creator
Please grant...

A tried true honest man
Not just one who says...
They understand!

A good girl & woman
No! A gifted Goddess
A spiritual yet Earthly woman

Mind having No grand schemes
Or far-fetched plans
Simple sometimes complicated

Job... Love Support
A bit of witty retort
Don't make life NO or sport

Many games are played
As others indulge
Why bother?

Not meant to walk alone: Isolated
Creator Guide heart, head & spirit

Being clean & sober understanding
Eventually, rewarded continued patience
A realization of unexpected kindness & love

An individual: intricate part of head, heart & spirit
Strengthen: Physically, mentally & spiritually weak
Loving arms & feet

(*continued next page*)

Not a dream or fantasy
It's what The Creator
Has shown and told to come

Positive wealth above beyond measure
A King & Master: The Creator
Wills for damn sure...

Never let...
A negative thought idea inkling
Defend nor question too matter

Not cuz of a need of approval or validation
But deserve every positive
Life has in store & offers karmic vibration

No mere words on a page or pages
Or written in any diary, novel or special book
Universal optimistic energy

Life defying comprehension
Sharing, exceeding greatest anticipations!

A child in a woman's body

Scared, mischievous,

sad & depressed

at times

Bold & defiant

As a
child:

did
woman things.

As a woman:

doing childish

child-like things.

Representative of self

View your judgment & distain

Make better choices in vision

See I be critical of this here behavior

Judge, Jury & Executioner

Hopeless Romantic

A Hopeless Romantic
The one dreamed about...
Only to believe
Far too good to be true

Nevertheless, a Hopeless Romantic
The one friends
Fantasize, yet warn about...
At the mental door
Knocking wanting beggin' to come in...

Still a Hopeless Romantic
Females taunt & despise
They laugh, maybe cackle, cut their eyes
They want to believe, sense it stupidity
Lover, Hopeless Romantics exist

Not a theory; a Hopeless Romantic
Still believe in old-time love & Romance
Believe in one spirit & mind: combined
Join-in in being a Hopeless Romantic

POETIC MOMENT

There are days thought...
However, it took time to realize
Never had any parts...
Never that smile, not depth of mind
No parts of broken shattered heart
Everything on loan or borrowed time

Don't even know of words
True or false
If every word
Part of some game
A plot, plan or scheme
By any means
Build esteem crush it with a blow

How does one expect to stay?
Feelings expressions pushing away
When every other moment
Choices to ignore
Ideally not mine
In separate lanes, different doors

(continued next page)

Wishing... No ill will
The wish... Love, laughter & understanding
Never ever feel pain
Guilt, shame & blame in loving another
One who... builds without intimacy
With one who has none in their mind

Poetic Moment: A love of words
Rise a voice & hands
Mark Twain put it best.
"Go to Heaven for the Climate
And Hell, for the company."
Don't know if it be true or false

This may seem a Goodbye letter
No just words & expressions
On a page or screen
Whether thought or care to remember
Remember what has been...
On both ends; It's all a relative perspective...

LOVE SONG

Independent far too long
Not much of an investment
No one to tell tales too
Just being…
Mostly entertainment
Answer to The Creator alone

Sheer desire to hold
Just the thought of a hug
Wrapped in warmth during cold
A young love even when old
Yeah grab hands
A pick up, pulled close
A love till the end

A true blessing
Swear to be good
Done looking for a future in a man
A time oh so right
We're here, right now
This simple LOVE SONG

Don't really like big crowds
Tend to shut people out
Space, yeah
Thinking of a soul mate
Creator has given life
Worth every waiting second

Just a love song
Every note & melody in tune
When hurt; known
A simple love song envisioned:
  HOPE STRENGTH LOVE EMPOWERMENT GROWTH

DAMN THE TEMPTATION!

Tormented desire
Fueled filled feelings kindle a fire
Kinda vexed & perplexing
Mind & emotions mystified
Tempting attempts

A breakdown of defenses
What anxiety of senselessness
Mind aflutter; Words shutter, stutter
Falling to knees

Kinetic energy a synergy
It surges right thru
Want to resist it persist
Such an existence

Shakes to the core
Uncut and raw
What of giving in…
Like a sin; Forbidden yet appealing

Confusion dwells
Spirit swells
Surrounds with presence
Yet, no true evidence of authenticity

(continued next page)

Tremendous tenacity
Defined in the pursuit
Words & actions shoot; Comforting a soul
How does one not lose control?
Letting them inside

Is it fear or pride?
Keeping mindset impetuous
Is the same song being sung?
A mirage or an oasis

Dip, dodge; the same temptations
Want this…Heart in flux
Desiring a touch; Ease back
Will charms slip thru microscopic cracks
What assumed a solid foundation?
Damn, the fucken temptation!

In Mind

Imagine seeing each other,
Holding another's hand.
Only to stare the other down,
Our perspective of what we were...

It doesn't matter either way,
In the past wished for a call by name.
What was done or said; Ain't nothing to change.
Apart, out of the others life... Or with another...

They say when love of something; Let it go.
If it comes back, then it means so much more.
If it never does, the answer was sure,
It's something most go through to grow.

Feeling this way,
Won't let anyone knock off this crown
In heart, in mind.
In soul, in mind.

Mysteries of the unknown,
Thoughts, of an insane cynical creation.
Always in prayer of one's mind.
There, somewhere

In mind, surely a good girl.
In mind, always a Goddess
Only time tells if someone's lady.
In mind, Not just anybody's Queen.

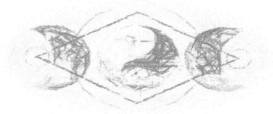

EROTICA

"Why should I be ashamed to
describe what nature was not
ashamed to create?"

~Pietro Aretino

DESIRE

Bathe in waters of milk & honey
Pour down like rains of the Amazon
Defy laws of time & space
Locked away our own personal getaway
Feed off one another's souls
Nourish tender ailing flesh & spirits
Climax: erupting volcano
Reach heights thought unimaginable
Collapse in ecstasy: intertwined anatomy
Blood lust in eyes
Gaze deep into unconsciousness
Revive through erotic essence
Experience savagery over & over
Days meld into nights
Nights burn as hot embers
Reignite fires even with limp physiques
Hunger - more, more, more

Take a 5 boroughs tour
Exploring creating wild fantasies
Fundamental atmosphere to heighten
5 senses of our being

First stop, Coney Island
Vibrant lights
Spectacular view of a distant horizon
Magnificent vision of what I have
YOU!

A visual probe of two bodies
Yours and mine
Eventually intertwined
Only a look
NOT to hear, touch, taste or smell
A *SIGHT* of pure majesty

Second stop, Yankee Stadium
The roar of the crowd
Hope and sheer delight
Whispers in my ear
Sounds of expectation

Just a simple part
My experience of YOU
The moans untainted groans of passion
Squeaks screams
The beat of our hearts
HEAR the exhilaration

Midway thru, Mid-Island Park
Playgrounds of fun
Supersized games
Grass between hands and thighs
Touching to experience life
My hand in yours   (*continued on next page*)

Eager to make exotic erotic traces
A daily experience
Cuddling rubbing caressing
If I choose, most cases I do
Examination through our *TOUCH*

Almost home, Penn Station
In and out of caverns
Cologne sweat musk
The scent of travel
Nomads & city dwellers lie

NO fear of discovery
Down low
Nose in creases
Taking in your essence
Neck and intimate spaces
SMELL seductive sensual places

Last NEVER least, Astoria
Ultimate destination
Appetizing cuisine
Greek, Italian or Thai
Feeding our palate

Thirsting hungering tastes of YOU
A purely carnal sexual mood
Tongue worthy salivation
Sweetest nectar
Tantalizing my *TASTE* buds

WOW!!!

A stimulating journey
An excursion ALL our own
The phenomena of my 5 senses
Immersed into your 5 senses
What a ride!!!

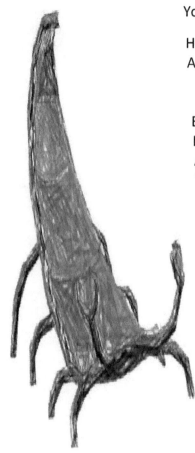

You're gym equipment

Head to toe
An aerobics workout
    A gasp

Breathing frequently shallow
In need of O^2
A rock willing to climb
Visual work of art

Love it when you say,
    "Baby, don't start!"
Motivation to get a body in
motion
Sleek tone curves: *TIGHT*

Keeping it raw savage
unreserved...
OMG... so satisfying

Surrender

The rhythm of a heartbeat
A pulse which throbs in one's veins
An antidote that frees all pains
'Til this point life's been incomplete

Twilight & Obsidian nights
Baby, fill every cavern
Movements penetrate
Body, gasps screams of ecstasy

Fingers touch caress
  Breasts
   Navel
    Thighs
     OMG, much, much more

Essence tastes of bitter sweet chocolate
  Kisses
   Tongues
   Enter
    Devour all morsels of being

Surrender
  Just to be conquered

In a low soft voice Candyse whispers to Jeremy, "Baby, it seems the morning has come entirely too soon." The sun slowly creeping over the horizon. She awakens to find the sun peering through a small slit of tapestry in the window. Or could it have happened from their night of exhilaration and sheer ecstasy which created the gap? She beholds how the sun touches Jeremy's face so gently, almost as if an angel endows heavenly blessings. Whatever the situation; the sun's rays beaming as it caresses his sleeping face. She turns toward him; eyes fixating a touch as his eyes open as she feels "I bear witness to one of the finest specimens of a spectacular man." She is taken aback. A smile glides across her somewhat sleepy face. She leans up and softly plants a kiss slightly below his open sleeping mouth. As soon as he feels it, he begins to tighten his arms around her. He kisses her on the forehead, only for them to drift back off into an additional short slumber. The night of events made them sleep so soundly, almost tranquil. It's nearing time for the lovebirds to depart from their love nest. Although, she doesn't want to awaken Jeremy she knows they have a long workday awaiting.

She couldn't get over how her plans for Jeremy were coming together. It was a day filled with excitement. Jeremy's birthday was a special time. Its importance goes without question; the day to come together to celebrate the gift The Creator has granted: *Life*. They both felt a tremendous capacity to pass blessings of hope and inspiration to others and especially one another. Candyse wanted to make Jeremy's day one he wouldn't forget and truly special as she could... She decided to go online and purchase a few things to set a critical romantic frame of mind. She doesn't realize it at first, speaking out loud, "Huh, maybe a simple silk teddy celebrating the occasion in that eye-catching color he races toward almost like a bull; candy apple red?" As well as a few assorted sex toys, which may or may NOT be used that specific evening? (grinning hard) She begins to reminiscence of their past encounters. How would she out do previous years they've been together? She starts with an emotionally seductive prose. Although words usually serve her well... She says, "Why, oh why is it not the easiest task transcribing my feelings toward Jeremy on this particular occasion?" She's nervous and excited at the same time. Although, it's a task she gladly couldn't wait to spear head. When she envisions the possible results; a slight smirk or short-lived giggle happens. Shit!!! She'll even settle for a deep sigh of remembrance of their joys, followed by a slow shaking of her head. - (laughing to herself)

A sentimental thought comes across her mind "(Ok Jeremy, here I go; deep breath)-...Here it goes...You are amazing!" Candyse is almost clueless yet instill thankful of the position Jeremy has in her life. She can't but feel blessed and a bit cursed for the gift she has while they are close. However, when they must depart at times to go on to do things which better suit their living environment. "I am very grateful and feel blessed to consider you my lover and friend. Do you understand?" She continues her writing with the idea or just trying to make an effort to ensure he knows how he makes her feel and things he does for her.

However, when they are together, she can't seem to contain herself. She wants to touch him in places which are hidden by clothing and light. Their episode starts with them face to face, staring into each other's eyes. They caress and hug firmly so they could feel their hearts beating together in harmony. A few sensual kisses (in a tone just above a whisper) which says, "*I WANT YOU.*" "Your lips are so succulent; sweeter and juicier than any peach." The flavor of his lips and in his kiss just excites raw feelings of ecstasy. "I'm in wait of your tender kisses in places only seen in adult films. I want to feel your nature rise as we kiss under the pale candlelight." The mental images of the way his body moves, like a sleek panther on the prowl. "Oh baby, let me be your prey. My 5-foot 7 frame acting as an arena for the epic battle that ensues within what we feel and what we think we know."

Candyse's heart takes its stance, declaring feelings and peaceful unparalleled dispositions. While her mind rages and races with frustration, uncertainty and a level of displaced "reason". As a writer, she tends to manipulate vocabulary and concepts to her advantage that's always been an influential point to her art. Yet beyond all that drives her to be devilishly alluring charm or use of deceptive mannerisms through words. She is compelled to honor their undoubted foundation; the truth! Oh, the passion! They just couldn't seem make it out the door for his birthday. Almost like giddy teenagers grinding through clothing or newly-weds savagely tearing at each other's body parts as they got ready. Eventually, they managed to get dress and on the road.

They spent the evening with Jeremy's family and friends. By way of concerted efforts of Jeremy's mother Amanda and herself. All evening they touched and made passes at each other in seductive tempting ways. A festive time had by all in attendance. When they arrived back at their lavish home. As Jeremy proceeded to open the door Candyse stopped Jeremy "Round 2: I want to be candid about my unadulterated yearning for your sculpted body and brilliant mind", says Candyse. They stared at each other for a moment with pure lust. She slams Jeremy through the door and against a wall in the house giving him ravenous kisses to his body; head-to-toe. The control she thinks she has is all for NOT, undoing his pants slowly with her teeth. Some hesitation and anticipation are necessary for such a sensitive area. What waits is an alluring sensual fragrance. She breathes in his essence with enthusiasm; his smell intoxicating to her like a respectably aromatic stiff drink.

She places a kiss on his cock through his underwear with heat which overwhelmed permeated and penetrated through. What came to her mind at that moment was the thought, "if you can't stand the heat, stay out of the kitchen." (she chuckles to herself) She was in wait of his tropical fruit, slowly lowering his underwear where his penis seems to be almost in wait of the warmth of her mouth. She adorns continuous kisses to the tip of his cock. She opens her mouth putting her tongue out to lick him like a delicious tantalizing tasty treat. Eagerly yet with minor force she glides her tongue down his shaft, followed by more wet kisses on and around the head. She makes sure to glance up and hold his gaze every once in a while. She even adds a devilish gleam in her eye. The admiration to her king blows his mind. He says, "My Goddess, is this heaven?" She doesn't forget his balls—gently rubbing and clawing them with the tips of her nails and cupping them in her hand. She loves feeling the weight of his testicles, enjoys the feel of them. Almost like playing and twirling a set of Chinese Baoding chime stress balls. She increases the sensation tenfold where his moaning and groaning seem to intensify. She pauses only for a slight moment to position his cock back into her warm waiting mouth after she saying, "Damn, my panties are getting drenched just hearing your passion daddy!" She continues with a slow rhythmic motion; head-bobbing to and fro. The expectation is overwhelming at this point. He lets her know he needs and wants to be inside her. He wants to feel the warmth and passion of her volcanic walls.

She gradually crawls onto the bed, ass up, making sure he gets a good look. Then, she lies on her back, her legs spread, fingering herself. She removes her fingers from "Suzy-Q" they name Jeremy bestowed her private place and sucks on each finger- one by one. What a tantalizing taste.

A fine wine, an exquisite bouquet; more seasoned then her formative years. "You're getting kind of bold these days," Jeremy says, still standing in place. "Damn baby, I am so hard." He starts pulling his t-shirt over his head. His body is defined and engaging. He says, "I'm going to fuck the shit out of you." "Promises! Promises!", she says. Candyse sits up and pulls him toward her by his waist gently nudging him to his back. Jeremy's cock is as hard as titanium at this point. She could feel the weakening strength and heat of her thighs. Candyse thrives off Jeremy being her man in every sense of the word; aggressive yet endearing. She says in a seductive tone, "Just a lil taste daddy!" As she proceeds to slide Suzy up his chest and then sits on his face. She grinds on his mouth for just a few minutes; even though he brings her close to her edge of excitement. It isn't about her this day; it's his day to be pleasured and pampered. It isn't his normal to sit back and have her control the situation. However, Jeremy knows he can leave his pleasures in the imaginative and more than skillful hands of his lover and friend.

After they get close -licking, sucking, massaging, fondling and slobbering all over each other. They were ready to get down to business. A lot of people prefer doing doggy-style; she had no exception. However, Candyse and Jeremy liked to get low. I mean near to the ground like a couple of Bassett Hounds. You know the dogs with short legs that look like they're crawling instead of walking? She got down on all fours, on her palms instead of on her elbows. Candyse pushed her ass up in the air and waited for Jeremy to place both his legs on the sides of her ass. He always starts off grinding her slow and lovely; he picked up the pace. Candyse is overwhelmed and in awe by that shit! The way he wrenches her hair back; the way he lodges his nails into her ass cheeks; the way he places little nips—or sometimes light bites on her shoulders. Even the way he would softly seductively put his hand around her neck with slight pressure.

Candyse says in a low seductive tone, "Happy Birthday Jeremy! The world needs more men like you; I'm glad to have a man so sure...May you be blessed with many, many more years, Beloved!" As he moans, "Baby, I'm cumming! Umm babeee!" And she turns around quickly to take in his nectar only too confident to savor every drop. Where they both eventually fall out on the bed and cuddle up together: Big spoon & Little spoon.

CHOCOLATE WONDERLUST

Dreamed a dream
Fierce fantasy
Make-a-Wish come true

Chocolate wonderlust
Dynamic sexual power
Tingles of all extremities

Master lead
Control our bodies
Such partners we make

Epitome of a true muse
Encouragement creativity
Inspiration sheer motivation

Domination of minds
Universally intertwined
An antidote freeing all pains

A complex lifestyle
No pre-arranged scenes
Tasty nectar

Submit irresistible sensations
Devour all morsels of being
                    Conquer & surrender to another

CAN I

Can I have you?
Have you look in piercing eyes;
Get lost in a galactic soulful abyss
Can I have you?
Have you pull close;
Snuggled by hot coco skin
Can I have you?
Have you lick lips;
Kisses - deep slow penetrating
Can I have you?
Have you cherish a complete existence?
Can I, can I have you?
Have you lie down
Lounge inside awaiting arms, breast & thighs?
Can I have you?
Have you keep memorable thoughts in mind?
spirit, heart: total being
Can I have you?
Have you love - forsaking all others
Can I have you?
All too myself
Can I?

DIRTY MIND

In the night,
Left with imagination
Always taken hostage
Envision us locked intensely - eye to eye

Grab from within deep inside
Lustful embrace
Wreak havoc on supple flesh.
Kisses... WILD SAVAGE
Gauged
Deliberate
Passionate

Deeply imbibe one another
Melt at the touch of intense hands
Your command
A body to possess & operate
Manipulate it.

Master artisan.
Eyes continually locked.
Neither wanting to miss a single expression
Kisses incessantly ravage & devour skin

(continued next page)

Making walls ooze & flood
Reach my face...
Smell & taste wetness.
Only proceeding to lick every bead
Oh, such sexy lips.
Sheer desire... over the MOON

Deep sensual kisses,
One after another
Damn! The thrust
Tremendous lust
Every last ounce of strength
We cry out in ecstasy
Oh my God! This what heaven's like?

GRIMEY (ADAPTATION)

There's nothing pretty to say
This isn't pretty, flowery poetry
I want you, not…
Sweep me off my feet
And ride a chariot into the sunset
NAW, FUCK THAT...

I want you in a vulgar, selfish way
I hope you're not the timid type?
It's crucial you feel me
In that area of your extremities
Where exhilarations mingle with
A scarce suggestion of dread

I will have you!
All of you.
What I foresee...
Ain't NO kind of fairy tale for this

Hell: get on your knees
Scream obscenities: undying loyalty – mine
Reward: indifference
Hell with rhyme, reason, time or season

Respect; none needed today
I'll except obedience
Silence not part of the game
Claiming your will

I swear on any stand; you'll be broken
No seduction tactics
No form of tenderness,
Yield to domination & a deceptive smile
Believe: It will be my way

Coincidence or Destiny

It started out like any other day: early morning exercise routine and then a shower. The shower was the place Christine could spend getting her thoughts together and personal pleasure. Showers were where she held private homage and admiration for "Goddess" which is the nickname her ex Nathan called her treasure chest. She loved the name so much to represent her hot spot, it stuck with her. "Oh, why shouldn't I show personal appreciation???" she thought. She took very good care of herself; ate right, exercised, abundance amounts of water to keep her insides clean, plenty of rest and mediation. Though, on this particular day *Goddess* yearned! No scratch that; she ached to be caressed and explored.

However, a funny story came to mind before entering her bathroom toward her shower. It was concerning one Valentine's Day where her girlfriends; Kali and Theresa gave her a gift the first year of her divorce. They thought it would be amusing to give her a Shower Massage on this particular Valentine's Day. The card read, "Maybe this will work out YOUR kinks, EVERYWHERE!!!" "Ha, Ha, Ha!" The joke was on them or so she thought. On the other hand, the joke was on her, the shower massage endearingly became the next best thing to a sexual partner over the next 3 years i.e. her best friend. Christine adored the way her friend touched her, almost seem to stroke her and definitely put her at ease. It titillated and tantalized her every female sense. She utilized every setting; of course, her favor was on full blast for that hot box – *Goddess.*

Christine enjoyed the way the water would cascade down her breasts. The pressure settings of the shower massage excited her nipples to the point of standing at attention and enthusiastically thrilled every nerve ending of her body. She thrilled at taking the handheld massager off the wall mount and would slowly begin to run it down the rest of her body. It created a warm sensation which she couldn't distinguish from the warm water or "Goddess". Although, she knew once the sensation grew intensely stronger and stronger as she got closer toward her treasure chest. She leaned against the walls of the shower; shower massage in one hand and the other commencing to spread her lips wide to have it pulsate on her clit. Eventually only to buckle under the pressure of her orgasmic release, falling to her knees. The time just seemed to fly; before she knew it... There was a faint knock on the door. The alone time she recently treasured – turned to quickly rushing out of her bathroom to get her children ready for their day. Thankfully, there was always tomorrow. Luckily being blessed with organizational skills far surpassing top CEO's; planned for whatever weather or attitude... Everything her beloved children desired had been set out the night before... However, it was always her daughter who seem to interject attitude or be the most difficult. "Mom, why did you pick that color or this outfit? or Something?" Lord knows how much she loves her children; they seem to know just how to get her in just the right spirits to set the rest of her day – NOT. Although, as a woman there were some moments she would rather be awaken and start the morning in a different way.

Such as the way she used to be awakened? Awe, Nathan! What fond sexual morning memories they shared. Nathan and Christine started as rivals since grade school. Their parents kept saying, "You're fated to be together." She despised, Nathan! He despised her but always found ways to protect her. Yet, he always picked on her for the awkward looking young lady she was...The Nerd. Christine wanted to find that special someone. Whilst in grade or high school she never found anyone she connected with especially of the male persuasion. She just wanted a guy like her father who she viewed as a King.

However, all that changed in the start of their senior year. Usually every summer their families would spend it together. Unfortunately, that summer before senior year. Nathan spent it his summer on his grandparent's farm. Christine had developed in ways most young ladies dream of... The mind of a brain surgeon and developed the body of a Penthouse/Playboy playmate. Nathan seemed to become Adonis overnight. He worked out constantly in the time they had known him. Of course, Christine would never look at him the same way the other girls did...in a sexual way. She despised him, right? Though, when he walked in the school first day of school, she felt wetness down her legs that had never happened or felt before... She couldn't move from that spot. The view phenomenal to say the least and she was embarrassed. It took her best friends – They had to pry her from where she stood. That first day of the rest of their lives was the turning point for them or so she thought... They went to Homecoming in the fall, the prom in the spring. Their senior year seem magical to most, even them. They were an inseparable couple. They were married after college and had 2 beautiful children. They had that what some would call: old time love. They shared a love which seem would last the tests of time. Or so Christine thought? It was until Nathan didn't know how to keep it in his pant for the woman, he took vows with...

It's been 2 children and 3 years since Christine left Nathan for the other women. She could never seem to get him out of her mind. During their marriage Nathan pleasured her in ways you only read about in erotic novels or literature. Since, senior year he always had the power to make her wet, just with a certain look. He knew how to kiss her where it made faint and weak in the knees. Oooh! And that man made her cream, it sometimes even amazed him. He took his time almost as if he was doing a surgical procedure: methodical and calculated. He adored every inch of her body. He would touch, rub, caress and/or press his fingers into her undiscovered orifices which would take her to new highs. It was always just the right amount of pressure on every single spot. Whether he used his hands, lips, tongue, teeth and even "Bear" (the darling name Nathan had given his member). Their episodes would go on for hours. He would make sure she was overwhelmingly satisfied. In her mind, each time they made-love, it was like their first time; over and over – again and again. Though, he pleasured her to ultimate heights, the betrayal wasn't something she could get over. Nathan was her first and only lover. Now, reduced to a shower massage, only so much a handheld device can do when you've experienced that type of passion and ecstasy.

Christine's life was always planned to a tee: a set routine. However, there was one particular day her routine was thrown off course, all jacked-up. It was the day when she hit a pothole and got a flat. "Damn, Damn and Damn". After getting out the car and seeing the flat she thought to herself, "First thing, call the office, let them know I'll be late and push my morning meeting back by an hour and half or two?" While waiting to get someone on the phone from the nearest service station. There was a passing car playing, "Sexy Can I". "How rude of some people", she thought to herself while still on hold. Before she knew it an extremely attractive, young brotha pulling up near her asking if she needed any help. Just standing there she couldn't seem to get words to come out. He asked again, "Can I offer you any assistance, Queen?" He pulled his car in front of hers and got out anyway. He stated, "I'm always willing to help a lady in distress. Are you in distress?" All she could do is node, "Yes" and giggle like a teenage school girl.

He looks at the tire and rim. He asks, "Do you have a spare?" Christine motions toward the trunk. Regrettably when he opened the trunk there was no spare. She forgot; she took it out. "Damn, damn and damn – Sorry, it slipped my mind to put the spare back in the trunk." He proceeded to call someone to pick up her car. She told him, "It wasn't necessary. I was in the process of calling my assistant for a tow truck and taxi before you arrived. But I thank you." He waited with her. There was lots of witty banter and sarcastic remarks between the two. He continued to insist on taking her anywhere she needed to go. He says some cornball line which must worked because she was off the phone, in his car until the tow truck had loaded her car on a flatbed. Even though, still in wait of her taxi. In her mind he was now her knight in shining armor in the black Audi. She eventually gave in and told him where she was heading. Him, "I know exactly where that is..." "Huh?" her. "Where you want to go." He says. Her mind only seems to wonder! The drive which usually took her a while to get too had gone by in a matter of minutes. They finally pulled up in front of the office building.

Throughout their entire encounter NO names were ever exchanged. Ultimately, he introduced himself. His name was something out of a romance novel with similar detailed characteristics – *Cannon Casanova*. Christine thanked Cannon for the ride (a dirty thought came to her mind. How she wanted to straddle him like a horse.) She was so appreciative of his generosity in helping her, she tried to offer him money. However, he was a true gentleman and denied. She walked into the building goofy as a schoolgirl with a Cheshire cat grin without ever telling him her name. She settled into her desk with a cup of tea. Her thoughts kept wandering back to Cannon; NOT being able to get him out of her mind. She hadn't felt so excited about or around another man since her divorce.

She thought about what she wanted him to do to her. The ways she would pleasure her newfound Adonis. She fantasized about the places and positions they would have their episodes and excursions. More and more thoughts stirred; how she had never been the kind of woman to talk or contemplate dirty. Yet, she felt the urge with him in mind. Things she never wanted to try or do with Nathan she wanted to do with this complete stranger. Her sexual appetite was so pinned up; remember 3 years. Until now, she felt overwhelmed and overdue.

The time breezed by because before she knew it her assistant was lurking in the doorway, clearing her throat to get her attention. The appointment she had rescheduled from the morning had arrived and been waiting. Christine couldn't get over the ridiculous grin her assistant had on her face. She commenced to ask her to send the client in... Too her surprise when she glanced up, it was Cannon. He stood there just as amazed... "Please have a sit. Can my assistant get you anything; water, tea, coffee or maybe me?" "Damn!!! She thinks to herself, "Did I say that out loud? Hopefully, he didn't hear the last part." She knows Lisa does as she giggles under her breathe. Where she says," Me too!" And lingers in the door with a slightly devilish grin. Cannon respectfully declines and says, "Maybe later to a combination of the two." Letting Lisa know in a stern voice, "Okay, that will be all." Lisa couldn't help but remain in the doorway far longer than she wanted. She wasn't even mad at her for doing so... "Shit, if I was any woman, I would do the same.", she thought. Just imagine one of those magazines model types or soap opera guys. The man was fine! He was standing slightly beyond the entry. She watched him walk to the chair; it was like watching the Discovery Channel when they filmed a panther in the wild on the prowl.

He sat in a chair directly across from her desk. She could see what seem to be a massive bulge from the angle he situated the chair. He began discussing how she came highly recommended by one of his closest corporate associates. They went over his prospective business plan and what he hoped to accomplish partnering with her firm. However, she felt it extremely difficult to conduct a professional dialogue. She was easily side tracked by everything he did and said. What brought her back was when he said, "I couldn't get you off my mind." He wanted to know if he could see her again outside of their professional venture or maybe another distress call. They both chuckled! He felt it was fate and no coincidence which brought them together; first the flat and now the meeting. As he spoke, she couldn't stop fantasizing about his lips. The possible ways he might kiss her and where... How they would feel on her lip, even Goddess. Frequently, losing focus at an alarming rate, every tone and articulation of the words he spoke made her want to jump across her desk and ravage him. She could feel her panties get moist, begin to soak the chair. Her treasure chest tingled and pulsated like a drum. The feeling closer to an explosive nature. Cannon had no idea what he was doing perpetuating in the brain to her lower extremities. She sensed her hands sliding down between her legs wanting to touch herself. Regrettably, she had to be professional remain composed.

He seemed to get restless because before she knew it, he got up to glance out of the window. Christine initiated to daydream again. The image of him strolling over to her and standing in front of her. It was pure temptation. She sits back in her chair seductively licking her lips. She gazed up with what she knows would give the impression of a devilish grin. As she leaned forward his zipper seemly direct in mouth and eye shot. He didn't object! She definitely had no gripes of what was in view. She held his hips with both hands, unzipping his pants with her teeth. No objections given! The miniature Cyclops: thick, long and strong met with her lips. She teased him with soft wet kisses. Gradually, she worked in the use of her tongue. It was similar to one who saviors ice cream on a mildly not hot day. Increasing as she takes him into her mouth, a lil deep throating here and there... He no longer wanted to contain the beast; the force and warmth of her mouth cause him to moan out loud in ecstasy. His rapture only motivated continued movement of pleasuring and passion. She was in wait of the explosion and savory taste.

Christine couldn't believe she was doing this... Especially, since Nathan had been the only lover in her life. Or was she really doing this? She knew she wanted and needed too. Just that fast, Christine snapped out of it. Cannon still talking about expectations of their merging interests. However, Christine in her own other world sat with her Cheshire cat grin continuing to visualize and daydream.

I TRIED

Papi, a Rub?
Love – Head-to-toe

Tantalizing savoring every morsel
  Use of hair, nose, fingertips
Definitely lips, tongue, even teeth

Provide ultimate pleasures
  Blissful elation
Deserve & seek

Coming back for more
  Each time unsure
Further, faster, giving more

Advancement
  In certain moods
Chase away blues

A King & Master of a Universe
  Goddess & Queen
Doing a thang

To compensate
  Gratify 'til we've had our fill
Exotic, carnal, phantasm shit

Unlike any other
  Do what NO one before
Has or ever done; willing to do again & again

Cry scream whisper just this name
  Baby, everyone wants the same
Give a chance to show even a Romantic side

If it's not enough…
  Can honestly say…
"DAMN PAPI, I TRIED!!!"

MENTAL SEX

Loneliness pushing sex into over drive.
Long for lingering wet kisses
Salivation of wetness

Images of body being taken over
Strong masculine hands caressing
Procure flesh

Shutter of thoughts
Legs being braced wide open
Lower lips: kissed, sucked with aggression

Eyes roll back
Imagination takes hold
Vibrant feelings cerebellum captivity

Loins throb in anticipation
Each mental stroke feels real.
Becoming; wetter and wetter

Masturbation makes longing stronger
Doesn't calm urges deep within
An actual touch satisfying sexual appetite

A dehydrated, neglected spirit.
Picture strong hands grasped firmly
Applied pressure around throat
Just the right amount of weight
Light headed, drunk with euphoria.

Night after night
Thoughts bury themselves
The fissures of the brain

Yes, oh yeah! Yearning more intense

APHRODISIAC

Voice of an aphrodisiac
Only to speak a name
Gesturing an answer
Telling our wants desires & needs

Through sexual expression
The answer to every question
Ever known about love

Without words
Use of our tongues to tell a tale
Kneeling…
Eyes feast upon pure masculinity
All its divinity
Too praise
All for self?

We begin to indulge
Digesting decadence
It drips the chin
Taste - Godiva couldn't re-create

Needing every atom of the anatomy
Necessity placed like a silver platter
The source of fortune
Plunging in and out

Stroking more than consciousness
Subconsciously rewinding love scenes
Daydreams, dreams, fantasy

(continued next page)

Seeing that face when we're making-love
It makes me want - here, there, then and now

Thinking of inappropriate places
Get tangled in sensations of private locations
Caught in a rock and hard place
No denying the advances

As wetness develops down legs activates to open
The spot a backdraft
Wanting to be extinguished
Know this body like the back of a hand
Touching - Sending ambiances of ecstasy

Thighs quiver
Anticipation of deep penetration
Heart rate rising
Sweating
Panting
Hands around my neck
Pulling hair
Wanting hickeys scratches on back
Uttering four letter words
In a four octave-range
Screaming only your name

We Fuck!
Speak in tongues: bilingual and/or multilingual

Aye papi.... Eres tan duro, me lo das oh tan delicioso, un
pecado mortal.
English Translation of Spanish
"Oh Daddy… You're so hard, you give it to me oh so
delicious, a mortal sin."

(continued next page)

Tongue between hips, thighs & lips
The struggle - Lick
Torture
Not really... Never ready

Running out of room
Begging for more
Crawling the bed frame
Up against walls

Prying thighs
Willingly submitting
Loving the ways of domination
Demanding cum
Do as told...

Molded...
Good to no-one but YOU
Conquering a once orgasmic-less world and multiplied it
Again, again and again

Face radiates with an after-glow
Pillows scented by us
A haunting fragrance
The room smells of the best sex
Ours!!!
Covered in body and finger prints
Name permanently written upon anatomy
A genetic marker

POWER OF A PRESENCE

Just thoughts...
Inner walls salivate; moist wet tongues
Anticipation of exploration
Kisses juicy: savory sweet peach
Run down lips after the first bite

Trespass on this body
Ignition at first contact
Power of chemistry
Forge floods
Souls flame an electrical impulse
Explode as vibrant firework

Face in scared erogenous zones
Climb; bed frames & walls
Tongue sings a song
A dance within

Do things....
No other has ever done

Creative rhythmic motions
Bodies expand and contract
Ecstasy cause uncontrollable reactions...
Engulfs every extremity

Not present....
Thoughts play in mind... over & over
Plague, torment, relish the other physique
Preference of another presence

Incredible!!!

> "Fool." said my
> muse to me. "Look
> in thy heart and
> write."
> ~Philip Sidney

Once
Upon
A
Muse

FACE

Awe of a face
Still not over
Oh, how lucky blessed of such a face
A smile which breaks through rain
Like over caste and winter nights

Come all the way on any given night
Just to look into eyes
Willed by grace all the way
Just to see such a smile

Holds like a swaddled baby
Wipes away tears... Kisses caress
A brilliant summer sunset sky
Illuminating moonlight
Every time we talk... "It's alright!"
And every time we talk... More satisfying

What a face
Oh, what Heaven has shown
When in need... Someone to love
Patiently stays... Shown not alone
Given a quiet kind of love
Behind such a kind generous face

In poetry show the world
Show the world the beauty
The stars and sun are jealous
Steal the sky of its light... Bring it aside
Steal the sky with that smile
Bringing light

Some are that face
The Creator deemed worthy
Given what's needed: One Another
Someone to love
In their sexy forgiving face

MASTER

Wishing for a call last night
Let someone know love and care
Except for the committee in mind
Is there something?

Wish it may, hope it might
Tired of running...
No other heart to call home
Forgetting what love feels like...

A touch...Gladdened to heart and soul
Looking for an ecstatic high
The feelings never felt oh so right
Only to bump into the man on the moon

Gotten purchase, No returns
What a spell...seeing that smile
Outta control...Reason to be
Romantic rendezvouses

This isn't wrong
May be hard to read
Wanting to just get along
Let down defenses
Just a chance to breathe

Admit it's a bit odd
What a way from jump
Incredible mindset...
Seemly, entwined by design at the start

(continued next page)

Conquer worlds
Never felt such exhilaration
Nobody's wrong
Somebody wishes to be right

Don't let go
Look toward future or growth
Outta control...Every reason to be
Impressions of sheer ecstasy

A submissive in need of a master
Puppet...control the strings
Need only to trust, Allow protection
Shape...Kiln this form
Is Euphoria conceivable?

Extra! Extra!
Read all about it
Got a Jones
For a pure work of art

Extra!
Extra!

Maybe a jaded perspective
Delicate palette extremes
Down to Earth
Interstellar grind, positive mind

Generously Sexy Satisfying
Our daily weekly monthly climb
Walls of excitement
Screams breaking barriers

Sheer addiction
Not a sickening affliction
Loving Lusting
Deep down into one's marrow

Hopeless Romantic
No dream
Some fantasizing
Wishing NO more...

Heavenly Romance
Trove of treasures
Experiment! Exhale!
Experience! Explore!

TRUST & BELIEVE

When laid to sleep
Ask of The Creator
Souls to keep

A day anew
A life tangible and resolute
Conviction in a Creator
Who's given a special man

One entrusted
Has no apprehensions
Embrace as authentic...US

Challenge of one's dreams?
Every whimsy
Make-a-Wish could fulfil
Once imaginative... now apparent

Believe in words, assured by actions
With mutual agreeability
Absolute satisfaction

Even when asked NO questions
Exhibit ideal honesty
Voluntary thoughts
At the end of the day... open-minded

(continued next page)

Why, not trust such an open book
A prize and exquisite jewel
Pirates and treasure hunters' thirst to plunder

No mere trove or artifact
A bona fide bounty; as a matter of fact
Deserving a love in this world
As well as the next

Merit faith, aspire affection
Be what dare dreamed of...
Trust? Believe?

YOU ARE POETRY

Our movements
Poetry, Music in motion
Cinema Picturesque view
Art in raw rare form

Meshed to create
Beauty only too make
Animalistic at times
Savagery to the core

Love & Lust Interwoven
Alpha: male & female
Nubian King & Queen
Quiet storms
Muses of inspiration

Unfounded doubt
Even the sound
Pathetic & irrational
To a sane mind

As we pursue apart or together
Light of our way
Strengths for out tasks
Peace for our worries

Unspoken Exchanges

Eyes that speak volumes
A voice only a tortured soul understands
Smile that touches parts not visible
Yet, unshared with the world
A chosen few to experience
Touch that tells needs vs wants: desires
Admitting in soft subtle strokes
Somethings of love
What's ungiven by others
Heart big as the Universe
Although, locked away

Eyes tell a tale
Spin the yarn... Visualizing attentively
Smile not frequent but genuine
Not deceiving as outsiders
Touch that keep praying positivity
All those across & around
Something in the love making
A passion for uncontrollable experimentation
Something in such a heart
Deepest as the abyss of oceans & seas
An inspiration of strength & courage

KISS! KISS!

It started with footsteps
Having a style all its own
Striving growing
Leaps and bounds

Kiss, kiss the stars
Only the universe
Too understand

Understand the man
A plan far too grand
No mere mortal to comprehend

Greatness
Infinite galaxies
Minute people standing
Delaying the swag & sway

Not knowing what's meant to be
An ultimate
Destiny fate
No fantasy

Continue to cause a commotion
Fast paced
Others in slow motion
Us in hypnotic trances

Take a stance
They all puppets
Not theirs
Make them dance

Secret: Key to divine devotion
Beyond great expectation
Simple uncomplex... Understand
Ask Believe Receive

Creator in infinite wisdom brought: YOU
A true inspiration
An intoxicating elixir
No meager hallucinogenic drugs
Its effects an unexplainable high

An unlimited sensation
"With great power comes great
responsibility"
A real true champion
Exceedingly: Lifting up up up
Above beyond mere words or
expressions

In life we hope to learn valuable lessons
Strength given some
A vessel of sincerity
Pulling many through
The burdens of pain & fear

Healing the ails
Conquer the veil to thrill
Live to thrive not just survive
Sheer ecstasy & passion
Chills to the bone

No need to scratch
Adventure doesn't linger
Only blooming
It's never consuming
It presses on

(continued next page)

Each day more enticing
Captivating
A bit intimidating at times
Loving endearing presence
An ultimate talent

Wanting to give the finest
Rarest of treasures
Sometimes lost,
gratefully found
The Loss Arc coming to mind

Patience needed in one's corner
Abundance of tolerance warranted
A blessing from above
Worthy of celestial gifts
A messenger of valuable attainable love

MAN OF STRENGTH

DEMI-GOD & KING FOREVER CLOAKED
BATTERED DENTED BLOODY ARMOR
RESPECTIVE STRENGTHS
DETERMINED LEADERSHIP

REINCARNATE: LEADERS MILITANTS PAST
HOLDING STEADFAST, YOUR PATH
RESCUE! RECOVER! RESTRUCTURE!
SALUTING THE JOURNEY

STRUGGLES ABUNDANTLY NUMBERED
INNOCENCE OBLIVIOUS
SHIELDING DEMONS
THEIR HEARTS, EARS & EYES
LIFE'S B-SIDE TRUE BATTLEFIELD

OTHERS DAILY EMOTIONAL TURMOIL
TEMPLATE YOUR PLATFORM & DOMINION
INGENIOUS IMAGERY THRU VISUAL MASTERY

ENEMY POSE AS FRIEND
STRATEGIC IN THE ART OF WAR
GREAT SUN TZU; DEPTHS OF ADMIRATION
SURRENDER! CONQUER! – NO IDEA THE WINS

GENEROUSLY COMPASSIONATE
YET, FEROCIOUS UNRESTRAINT
BABIES COO, FEMALES SWOON, ANIMALS???
ALL OBEDIENTLY RESPECTING
BURDENED SHOULDERS WHICH CAMOUFLAGE POWER

COLD SWEAT

Every time thought of...
Realize exactly what's been missing
How could one be so blind
And such a fool
Never to have listened

When together then...
Never thought about the love at the time
So, now sitting all alone
Longing for a moment just for a touch
But, not through loving yet

Love got a cold sweat going on...
So cold, oh the cold
A summer cold with similar winter chills
Cold sweat
Loved so good haunts with regrets

Nothing seems the same
When alone... All the memories
Memories of every hour; that first time
Every single moment after like the original time
Remember all those little text & notes

Those around say it's such a damn shame
Sorry such a bitter break & part
The things done
Create such a lonely heart

There are times feeling especially sad
Think of things done wrong & surely, right
The special times shared together
Knowing, wishing it would last forever

(continued next page)

Feelings craved to recall
Can't, don't forget
Secluded times of tremendous trepidation
Love got this mind, body & spirit in a cold sweat
Oh so, wrong for letting go
Did much wrong, take all the blame
Impart one more try baby
Can there be a beginning with no end again

Lonely woman until such a presence
Came along, black knight - eyes hurt &
compassionate
Felt led & wronged
Did wrongs too
Blind to see not a victim or martyr
Know the part played in the dram

There have been lessons & blessing learned
At the time too damn conceited
Never want to see things perpetuated
Not doing the journey alone
A personal physical presence desired on the path
Cease, help dry the cold sweat created
Bonnie & Clyde...Until the final fade to black

LICENSE TO KILL

Points; Goddess for a year
Not just wifey for a few nights

Thoughts appeared provoking
Though, bodies splif tree toting
Intellectual emotional masturbation
Both having verbal & visionary penetration

True God & diva: leather linen silk
The ride? Extreme in full tilt
Hips together swayed
Knees shook quivered quacked

Universal treasures
Kept it tight: trust Believe
Outta control, right
Point to motherfucking point blank!

Our mind for the game divine
Given multiple orgasms day or night
Cum no time touched any navel
Never imbibed spit slurped rivals

Asses were in psychological chains
Suck, oh fuck - Caught our breath
Panted moaned screamed
For that "Sexual Chocolate" optical nigga

Having No hint, no fuckin clue
Murderously killed with mental stimulation!!!
Visuals subliminally factual: GENUINE & WOKE
Envision a Power Couple with *A License to Kill*

No Mere Game

Appearing only as hallucination
Everywhere glimpses
Everything not what seems
A stranger, yet somewhat known

Sunshine in the rain
Wipe away tears
Kiss away pain & sheer misery
Everything...

Don't know why a runner?
Running away from devotion
Hiding wanting to withdraw
Although, alert to a potential find

Every time eyes closed
Can't get visions out of memory
Wishing sometimes wishing
Sentiment mildly subsides

Never aspire to push away
Realize, no aims to face another day
Life not the same
It's not a game

Given love longing to know
No doubt, Just crazy...
Don't want to live without
Yield to unconditional love

Cross oceans, seas, span galaxies: Reveal
Love, care, respect & admiration
Express through words
Actions demonstrate equivalent

RECOVERY

"When a storm is coming all other birds seek shelter. The Eagle alone, avoids the storm by flying above it. So, in the storms of life... May your heart soar like an Eagle."

~Unknown

MELANIN PRIDE

"Brown-skin" Indie Aria said with Pride
Dark melanin sistah's & Brotha's
Let's talk about our separation
Neither wanting to fathom the others struggles

Mixed breed child – not black nor white
Indignation of bias amongst all sort
Shamed about complexion
Can't seem to get from under tort

Drowning in other thoughts of lighter skin
Feel we're privileged many advantages within
Didn't create foul fierce beasts
Inferiority battles in our culture must cease

Centuries later mindset remains
House and field nigga playing different roles reign
All in the same twisted game
Again, both didn't ask it to be...

Robbed of native nationality
Field or house: Raped and stolen identity
No better or worse
Society tells us our skin a curse

Come On... Recognize the divergence
Let's partake in amended considerations
Identify; shed the stamps, labels & mutilation
Build upon once civil spiritual nations

(continued next page)

Ripped of languages taught another
Greatest Architects, Philosophers, Mathematicians
Great thinkers of ancestry Spiritual Shamanist
Still guide in dreams and strong intuition

Not an enemy or foe
Powers now - need & want us to believe so...
Mindset of confusion, chaos, disunity
For sustained conformity

Dark or Light: Continued inner turmoil
Curse blaspheme: How? Why made?
Our fight amongst the other
Just keeps us enslaved

No chains, shackles or whips
The brainwash is real for far too long
Some sing - Uncle Tom's song
Goal now: Love & support

It's No longer society or so-called hierarchy
We perpetuate and divide with apathy
Non-melanin masses front seats of grand sport
Smile in face, just holding court

There were those whom tried to bring us together
"See What's Going On?"
They're no longer present
Mysteriously taken educating fertile unblind minds
Accident, ailment or afflicted addictions reside

(continued next page)

Think it conspiracy theory
Start questions behind closed doors
Secret societies do furthermore...
The REAL meaning...

Never want melanin to roam free with knowledge
Kept boxed, labelled in mental bondage
Fatal incident may fall upon this body
Keep vigilant of true weighed economy

"Stop the Violence"
Let's change the nativity
Overwrite the brand standard; bitter slut or thug
Debunk, eradicate curse put on melanin antiquity

LIKE FLOWERS

Like flowers need sunlight
Care to make them grow
We need & want encouragement
More than we'll care or ever know

We need faith & bravery
Sunshine of a smile
Thoughtful assurance
Which makes life come alive, worthwhile

We want warmth & shelter
Loving arms & hugs provide
Most of all highly probable to know
We always can trust in a Spirit as a guide

MASK

I wear the MASK
It fashionably adorns my face
What mask? This mask?

During private moments
It sits in its proper place
A shelf or hook; just my special nook

The mask???
Why? You ask...
No mere accident or tragic incident
It's life... PAINS and FEARS

When in my home
I wander freely
No cares of this world

On cloud nine
A dance of grace
Away from time
Beyond space

Lonely
Wanting to explore
Anxious in approach
Slowly near the exit door
Yearning for love
Hungry for intimacy
A safe place

(*continued next page*)

Plagued by torment
Dark twisted tortured past
I wear the mask

Out in about
Suffocating restraint
Wanna breathe deep

Hiding shame
Only to gain
More pain
Continually to refrain

Hidden blame
Pooling tears
In slow motion
Time forsaking
Unforgiving

Ultimate wish
Shed and shatter the mask
Let go: fear and pain
Be brave
Accept TRUE self

A menace to society
Dangerous blight to self, the world

Pinky in need of The Brain
Stabilize an intent

Tears fall down
A monsoon, so much rain

What feelings?
Such pain?

Help me find sanity
Can't, don't have courage to live

A sacrifice? Life?
To live, be a productive part...

Constant torment
A tortures soul

No understanding
When? Why? How? Just roam!

Birth or cultivated
Wearing a mask all the same

No Labels

Put no labels
More than what one sees
Far more imagined being

Greatest & beyond anticipations
Character defects flaws inflated
Love or Hate

"Spiritual-Being having a human experience"
Experiences of struggle & conflict
Such blessings of grace

Mercy of The Creator
Purpose of inspiration to others
Unsupportive of loved ones at times

Caretaker even in the womb
Don't take kindness as weakness
See a side never want to see

No labels, PLEASE!!!
Blast of words cut of a double-edged sword
Direction straight forward

No sneak attacks
See it coming
Strategic mental tact

Some fooled by a demeanor
Pitbull/cobra locked loaded
Ready to strike

Nice or nasty
Depending the way lines cross
Crazy living an insane world

Ignorance of others unknowing
The cage created
Mental strong hold; deflection or a protection

DEMONS OF RECOVERY

On a path or journey of discovery
A part and parcel of recovery

Deconstruction of thoughts: present a negative civilization
Reconstruct a lost more positive civil nation

Why such mental fuckery & domination?

Outer limits present no challenge to others psyche –
       Compare or contrast
Inner turmoil continues – tricks or treats

Everyday a merry-go-round of destinations
Depression Fear Anger Elation
Never knowing what the mind may offer or seek

Comfortable with blame shame
Heart wallows in pain
The fault all the same

A glutton for punishment being the norm
Ever sick?
Mental mutilation masturbation penetrating to quiet the
storm

An inner voice – low voice screams: PEACE
The beasts?   Damn, these fucken beasts!

(continued next page)

Hyde, Hyde's alter-ego abound
Wait in shadows, the cut to reek
Mind oils the gates – a stealth sly sleek sneak
There is havoc which wants to ensue
Play victim martyr saint best as one can or might do

Some view it sick
A downright disgrace
Judge if you must as upside-down thinking

Honest Open Willing to rid or lock away
Trust Believe... Why this world is...
Or should be glad for tortured soul
Living in a solution of recovery

ANGELS AMONG US

Angels exist: Believe it!
Walking amongst us
Spiritual guides

Put us on a path
No destination
A journey of discovery

We deviate from our route
Do what we choose to do...
There is positive exploration

Unity, Service & Love
Provide great comfort elation

A reason
A season
Our lifetime of experiences

Take these hands
Point these eyes
Guide the way

Tranquility serenity ecstasy on Earth
When chosen
Yes, choose it!

No Vacancies

A possession
Bought not yet sold
A toy, play thing
Put on a shelf or something to hold
Keep it forever tucked away

Little misunderstood child
One who continued to be scold
Sadistic masochistic mentality
Extremely close friends
As wish survive tragic lives; out for a win

Can't call it selfish
We all want what we want
Wanting to master joy of a day
Principles before personalities easier way

Delusion all our own
Think self-more than that
Imaginary twisted mind
Many say crazy; true & bitter facts

Mind runs away; scattered brain
Thought fantasize, dream, hope
Can't understand why it wanders
Knowing where mind body soul chose
Wanting patiently, though

(continued next page)

No vacancies; mind body spirit
One design
Keep head, make it
No longer sick of lonely air

Much to get off & out of heart
Waiting tolerantly
Time seems to move slow
No vacancies; sheer honey & lustful bliss

Knowing what's Universally meant
Keep thoughts from wandering
A special design
It's to be greater later often told...

Once a land of Darkness
Speculations of the journey
Sure, of somethings
Others unknowing

Magnificent majestic land
Twists & turns
Ups & downs
Nowhere sure to roam

Slightly seasoned & aged
Continually rising
Growth & wisdom
Constantly striving

Endeavors toward improvement
Enhancement on willingness
Such wonderment positivity
A constructed lifetime plans

Founding; Uncontrollably not mine

SHEDDING TEARS

Even the clouds shed tears
Tears which flourish beauty or destruction
When these tears fall
There is a magic which can happen

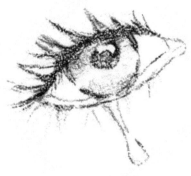

They give life
Strengthen roots sprout
Bloom flowers of beauty
With exotic erotic scents

When the sun shines
It may give birth to a rainbow
Shining across the sky
Brilliant colorful joyous

For whatever reason
Do not refuse the gift of purging
Shed tears anger frustration
Tears are strengthening

They need not destroy
Let the restoration commence
Gorgeous Handsome
Fabulous – YOU, Yes YOU!!!

MISAPPROPRIATION

Misappropriate culture, known vultures circle
Taken as one's own
Done since the beginning of time
Nothing changed; No rhythm or rhyme

Culture, History, Religion shattered to dust
Left in deserts & forest lands robust
Inspired poetry, music, alchemy, artistic visionary
Enslavement their imaginary

Misappropriation of many philosophies
Deceivers of pigmentation
Thief of nations; obliteration
No guilt, shame or remorse
Melanin societal castration

Genocide happening on a daily basis
Local, distant secluded places
Agenda strong, rigorously abrasive
Generational resilience
Split divide ancestral pride

White privilege; never seem to do time
Pay for crimes against colored humanity
Ours a woke perspective
Theirs a plea of insanity

Don't play the game
Not a lame brain, unfit any frame
Don't do this or that
One day slain through eminent domain

(continued next page)

Curves too much; buxom or fat
Hair too big, told too much nap
Locs, dreads, cornrows, waves or kink
Mane incredibly multidirectional
Comparable to startling potion drink

Antennas to a mystical threshold
Enlightenment, serenity
Acceptance of self to behold
Creator lifts the veil of unpleasantry

Continual degrading of Black Life intellect
Termed: lazy unmotivated angry bitter reject
Eternally locked; Fall will be from within
Centuries of experimental brain-washing

No longer held in metal irons
Yet, mental slave chains
Perpetuating diseased minds
Slept too long, wake the FUCK UP
Three or four generations not removed being sold

Fight never ending
In need of our knowledge comprehension
Intune if one listens
Guide direct positive intentions

Not an enemy
Sistah, brotha; Kings & Queens
If given lands promised indemnity
Let's unite heal build equity
Growth past historic catastrophes

EQUALITY

The People wavering drifting apart
Fighting colliding many deceitful hearts
Struggles profound
Tripping slipping clowning

Select few plotting scheming
Laugh as they place their grand plan
Politics Education divides
Destined to ruin simple lives

"The root of all evil, ain't money
It's the mind-state that put money before people."
No truer words spoken
In present time

Where is our Martin's, Malcolm's, Shirley Chisholm's?
Stand by our sides not on our backs
See what's going on?
We've lost our way

Let us NOT forget
Or doomed to repeat
Shit!!! We never stopped
The lie was shifted hidden up a skirt

Searching not finding
Anyone with positivity to say?

Those that are...
NO, NO, NO!!! Being murdered
Stop-n-Frisk, back woods & In streets
Give ALL lives not just death greater air time
                    Hope & Meaning

ABOUT THE AUTHOR

Chandra: Moon (चाँद) /mo͞on/
Sanskrit & Hindi origin
Noun
1. the natural satellite of the earth, visible (chiefly at night) by reflected light from the sun.

Born in Michigan, raised in New Jersey in the 70's. A current New York resident since the early 90's.

Moon, always feeling: *"A Journey Not a Destination"* is a self-portrait of experiences captured and perceived through a lens of poetry and erotic short stories. Written over a lifetime in search for identity and belonging due to years of childhood and adult traumas. However, feeling she had no voice or couldn't express herself. Writing became an outlet to escape, release and explore thoughts of all types of relationships with different circumstances, attitudes & behaviors.

This body of work was sparked by her two "Little Big People" - Niqué & Josh. They felt others could identify with the words scribed in journals: love, pain, sexual fantasy, hurt, anger, frustration, and much more encompassed, which challenged her to make the work publicly available.

***

"This journey of a lifetime started with the turn of a page, lash of pen to paper or stroke of keys to keyboard." ~Moon

* * *

May we continue our journey with a joyful heart and merciful spirit.

* * *

Made in USA - North Chelmsford, MA
1161684_9781734596298
09.09.2020 1435